Fire Drill!

A First-Start® Easy Reader

This easy reader contains only 65 different words, repeated often to help the young reader develop word recognition and interest in reading.

a
afraid
all
and
are
back
be
clothes
do
don't
drill
drop
fight
fighter
fire
Fred
friend
get
go
happens
has
he
here
hoses
how
if
in
is
it
it's
just
know
knows
ladders
like
line
lives
low
out
quick
quiet
roll
safe
save
saves
says
show
smoke
someone
something
soon
special
stay
stop
that
the
this
to
today
truck
under
we
what
who
you

Fire Drill!

by Janet Craig

illustrated by Rebecca McKillip Thornburgh

SCHOLASTIC INC.
New York Toronto London Auckland Sydney
Mexico City New Delhi Hong Kong Buenos Aires

ISBN 0-439-68722-5

Published by Scholastic Inc. SCHOLASTIC, TROLL, First-Start® Easy Reader, and associated logos and designs are trademarks and/or registered trademarks of Scholastic Inc.

12 11 10 9 8 7 6 5 4 3 2 1 5 6 7 8 9/0

Printed in the U.S.A. 08

First Scholastic printing, September 2004

Someone special is here today.
Who is it?

He has special clothes.

He saves lives.

And he is a friend.
Who is it?

It's Fire Fighter Fred!

“Don’t be afraid,” says Fred.

“Under this . . .

and this . . .

and this . . .”

It's just Fred!

And he is a friend.

Fire Fighter Fred saves lives!

He knows how to fight fire.
And he knows how to stay safe.

“If this happens,” says Fred,

“get out. And stay out!”

“If this happens,” says Fred,

“stop, drop, and roll.”

We stop . . .

we drop . . .

we roll.

“If this happens,”
says Fred,

“under smoke—we go low!”

Here we go.
Under smoke—we go low!

“Here is something special,” says Fred.

It’s a fire truck!

It has hoses.

And it has ladders.

The hoses fight fire.
The ladders save lives.

It's a fire drill!

Today we get to show what we know.

We all go out in a line.

We are quick.

We are quiet.

Do this!

And this!

And this!

“We are all here!”

Soon we go back.

We are quick.

We are quiet.

FD

"You know how to stay safe in a fire,"
says Fire Fighter Fred.

"You know how to save lives.
And that is special!"

“Just like you, Fire Fighter Fred!”